CW00797413

Original title:
Rough Sparks Under the Elf Wisp

Author: Olivia Orav
ISBN HARDBACK: 978-1-80562-740-1
ISBN PAPERBACK: 978-1-80564-261-9

The Everlasting Dance of Stardust

In twilight's grasp, the stars ignite,
Their whispers weave through the velvet night.
Each flicker tells a tale of old,
Of dreams and secrets, bright and bold.

They twirl and spin in cosmic glee,
A dance of light for all to see.
Beneath their gaze, the world stands still,
As wonder wraps the heart at will.

With every pulse, the heavens sigh,
A lullaby from realms on high.
In every shimmer, magic flows,
Where destinies align and grow.

Lost in this wondrous, glowing trance,
We join the stars in timeless dance.
For in this night, we find our place,
A journey wrapped in stardust's grace.

So let the cosmos hold us near,
In the embrace of dreams sincere.
Together, we will brave the night,
A tapestry of purest light.

Bursts of Enchantment in the Dappled Woods

In whispered glades where sunlight plays,
The trees perform their ancient ways.
With leaves like laughter, soft and sweet,
They hide the paths where fairies meet.

A gentle breeze—a secret sigh,
Awakens magic, passing by.
With every step on mossy ground,
A symphony of life resounds.

Beneath the arch of emerald leaves,
The forest breathes, and time believes.
In shadows deep and light's embrace,
We find the heart of nature's grace.

The mushrooms twinkle, dreams take flight,
Each corner glows with pure delight.
As fables unfold beneath the boughs,
We pause to wonder, to take our bows.

In dappled woods, the world feels grand,
Where every creature draws close its hand.
Within this realm, our spirits soar,
A dance with magic forevermore.

Flares of Mystery Beneath the Canopy

In shadows deep where secrets play,
The whispers weave through night and day.
Each flicker tells a tale unknown,
Of creatures that in dreams have grown.

With every step, the leaves align,
A dance of magic, pure, divine.
Beneath the boughs of emerald hue,
Adventure waits for hearts that true.

The moonlight spills like silken thread,
Entwining paths where few have tread.
A glimmer here, a shimmer there,
What wonders lie in twilight's care?

Among the roots where echoes lie,
The spirits of the woods float by.
With every flare that paints the air,
The forest sings its mystic prayer.

To wander is to find the key,
Unlocking realms of reverie.
In every rustle, every sigh,
The night reveals its ancient lyre.

Celestial Sparks in Enchanted Realms

In skies so vast where fairies play,
The stars above, like candles, sway.
Each twinkle is a wish bestowed,
A secret path where dreams have strode.

Through realms adorned in silver light,
The galaxies ignite the night.
With every spark, a promise made,
In whispered tones, the moonlight wade.

A comet's tail, a fleeting flight,
Across the heavens, pure delight.
The heart of magic lies in sight,
For those who gaze with hope ignited.

Within the depths of twilight's grace,
Lie hidden worlds we long to trace.
The air is thick with dreams unfurled,
A tapestry of magic swirled.

With lanterns bright on paths unseen,
We wander forth, where souls convene.
In every light, a story spun,
In celestial realms, we are all one.

The Glow of Wildwood Fantasies

In tangled woods where wishes dwell,
The air is thick with tales to tell.
Branches bend with stories old,
A canvas rich, where dreams unfold.

Each glimmering leaf a spark ignites,
Within the heart, it stirs delights.
Through misty paths where shadows gleam,
The wildwood holds a gentle dream.

From twilight's brush to dawn's embrace,
The forest wears a secret face.
With every breath, the magic swells,
In rustling leaves, enchantment dwells.

Beneath the stars, a dance begins,
Of woodland sprites and forest sins.
With laughter sweet and voices low,
The woodlands hum with mystic flow.

In every nook, a tale lies bare,
Awaiting hearts to stop and stare.
As fantasies in whispers glide,
The wildwood dreams, forever wide.

Chasing Starlit Whispers

In twilight's hush, the stars awake,
With secrets that the shadows take.
They sprinkle dreams on silent night,
As whispers dance in silver light.

We chase the echoes of the past,
Through shimmering paths, so vast.
Each star a guide, each glow a sign,
Leading us to the divine.

In every glimmer, stories weave,
Of hearts alive and dreams believe.
The night's embrace is warm and wide,
With starlit whispers as our guide.

On velvet skies, our hopes are pinned,
In cosmic tales that never end.
Through realms where fantasy blooms bright,
We dance beneath the gleaming night.

So take my hand, let's find our way,
Through starlit paths where wishes sway.
In every moment, magic lives,
In chasing dreams, the heart believes.

The Fray of Magic's Embrace

In shadows deep where whispers play,
The ancient spells begin to sway.
With flickering lights, the night unveils,
A world where hope and fear exhales.

With wands aloft, the brave unite,
They dance with spirits through the night.
Each flicker sparkles, a promise of dreams,
In the heart of magic, nothing's as it seems.

The winds of change stir whispers high,
As destinies weave 'neath a starlit sky.
With every heartbeat, a tale unfolds,
Of courage found and secrets told.

In shadows cast, a bond is forged,
With every challenge, their strength enlarged.
Together they rise, as one they soar,
Through darkened paths, they seek for more.

So hear the call of magic's might,
Embrace the fray, embrace the light.
For every journey, both fierce and brave,
We find our purpose, we learn to save.

Glimmers of a Forgotten Lore

Through dusty tomes and faded signs,
Lie echoes of long-lost designs.
In quiet corners, secrets hide,
Waiting for hearts that dare to stride.

With candle's flicker, shadows dance,
Revealing the tales of fate and chance.
In every letter, a whisper swells,
Of bygone times and mystic spells.

Each flickering thought a thread to weave,
A tapestry where dreams believe.
Through winding paths, the lost ones roam,
In search of truth, in search of home.

So pen your hopes on parchment bare,
Let ink flow free with endless care.
For in the words, new worlds arise,
Beneath the watchful, starlit skies.

In long-lost lore, the heart finds grace,
In every story, we find our place.
With glimmers bright, the past awakes,
In shining truth, as magic breaks.

Shimmering Echoes of the Unknown

Beneath the waves where dreams elude,
The echoes sing in waters crude.
With shimmering lights that bend and sway,
They guide the lost on their secret way.

In twilight's hush, a call rings clear,
Awakening spirits, far yet near.
Through veils of silence, time unfolds,
Revealing secrets that fate upholds.

Each ripple carries a whispered sigh,
As shadows dance beneath the sky.
With every heartbeat, paths intertwine,
As shimmering echoes, stars align.

Embrace the unknown, let courage shine,
For in the dark, the light is thine.
In every shadow, a glimmer waits,
To guide the soul through destiny's gates.

So listen close to the night's embrace,
In shimmering echoes, find your place.
With dreams aloft and hope renewed,
The unknown glimmers, brave and shrewd.

Dashing Dreams Through Twilight Veils

As twilight descends with a violet glow,
A tapestry of dreams begins to flow.
With laughter bright echoing free,
They dance through realms of fantasy.

Beneath the moon's soft, watchful gaze,
The world ignites in mystic haze.
With every step, the dreams take flight,
In gentle whispers of the night.

With starlit paths that twist and wind,
Hearts awaken, eager and kind.
Through twilight veils, they weave their schemes,
A symphony of dashing dreams.

Together they soar on silken wings,
Emboldened by the joy that magic brings.
In fleeting moments, they chase the spark,
Through shrouded realms, through light and dark.

So raise a toast to the fleeting hour,
To dreams that bloom like a magic flower.
For in the twilight, all is revealed,
Through dashing dreams, our fates are sealed.

Elusive Gleam of Enchanted Realms

In twilight's hush, where shadows play,
A whisper lingers, soft as clay,
Through silver woods, where secrets hide,
The heart of magic, deep inside.

A river flows with starlit dreams,
Each ripple holds a tale, it seems,
With every glance, a flicker bright,
Unlocking doors to hidden light.

The breeze sings songs of days gone by,
Where laughter danced beneath the sky,
In every leaf, a story spun,
Of ancient quests that never run.

Beneath the moon, the fae do tread,
In circles where the brave are led,
With courage woven in their hearts,
They chase the place where wonder starts.

And so we seek, through dusk and dawn,
The elusive spark that lingers on,
In enchanted realms, we find our dreams,
The world alive with magic's beams.

Magic Woven in a Thousand Gleams

In gardens where the starlight weeps,
And every bloom a secret keeps,
The air is thick with wonders rare,
As whispered wishes dance in air.

The tapestry of night unfolds,
As every thread of fate retold,
With vibrant threads in colors bright,
We weave our dreams into the night.

Within the heart of ancient trees,
Where time stands still, and troubles cease,
A melody begins to play,
In harmony, we drift away.

Through realms unseen, where spirits roam,
In every corner, we find home,
The magic dwells in fleeting sparks,
Awakening our truest hearts.

So let us gather every gleam,
And paint the world with every dream,
For in the magic, we shall find,
The threads that weave the ties that bind.

The Flicker Between Dreams and Whispers

In twilight's glow, the whispers call,
As shadows dance on ancient walls,
A flicker stirs, the night awakes,
Where dreams are born and silence breaks.

The stars above, like lanterns bright,
Illuminate the shrouded night,
With secrets spun in silver thread,
A gentle balm for hearts that dread.

The echoes of a long-lost song,
Invite us where the brave belong,
With every note, a truth to find,
Awakening the still confined.

Between the worlds, a pathway glows,
Where time stands still, and wonder flows,
In every heartbeat, magic swells,
Unraveling the guarded spells.

So tread with care, dear dreamer's heart,
For here, the worlds of old depart,
In flickers bright, our spirits soar,
Between the dreams we all explore.

Glorious Echoes in a Forgotten Realm

In lands where time and magic weave,
A tapestry of what we believe,
The echoes of a bygone grace,
Whisper softly in this sacred space.

Here, ancient stones hold stories tight,
Of battles fought in the heart of night,
With every breath, a sigh releases,
As history's chorus softly ceases.

The winds carry tales of old,
Of heroes brave, and treasures bold,
In every rustle, a dream unfurls,
Creating ripples in hidden worlds.

Amidst the ruins, hope takes flight,
A phoenix rises from the night,
With glorious echoes, hearts reclaim,
The spark of life, the warmth of flame.

So wander here, in twilight's gleam,
For within shadows, we can dream,
In forgotten realms, our spirits call,
Where magic reigns, and love unites all.

Whispers of Ember in Twilight

In twilight's warm embrace, the embers glow,
Soft whispers weave through the night's gentle flow.
Stars awaken, stitching skies in golden thread,
While dreams carry secrets that words have not said.

A shadow dances lightly, on the edge of sight,
Carried by breezes that flicker with light.
With every heartbeat, the world holds its breath,
As time slips away, teasing us with death.

The trees start to rustle, as stories unfold,
Of heroes and journeys, of legends retold.
A flicker of magic, like embers in flight,
Whispers of hope shimmer through the night.

With every soft sigh, the darkness gives way,
To promises woven in twilight's ballet.
Through the mist, we gather, hearts open wide,
Through whispers of ember, together we glide.

So linger a moment, let the dusk draw you near,
With shadows and light, let go of your fear.
In whispers of ember, let your spirit ignite,
And dance through the stories that dwell in the night.

Glistening Shadows of Enchantment

In a glade lost in time, shadows softly creep,
Where moonlight glistens, secrets gently seep.
Enchanted whispers paint the night in gold,
As stories of wonder and magic unfold.

The trees sway in rhythm, their branches entwined,
Holding close the dreams that the stars have aligned.
A soft breeze carries a melody near,
As glistening shadows dissolve every fear.

From the depths of the forest, a flicker ignites,
Awakening spirits that dance in the nights.
With laughter like chimes and songs pure as rain,
The glade wraps around us, erasing all pain.

In the hush of the night, we gather as one,
Beneath the soft glow of the mournful moon's sun.
With eyes shining bright, like lanterns they gleam,
In glistening shadows, we weave through the dream.

So come, take my hand, let the magic unfurl,
Through glistening shadows, let our spirits whirl.
In enchantment we wander, as hearts intertwine,
In the echoes of night, your dreams will be mine.

The Flicker of Fantasy's Edge

On the brink of a dream, where fantasy sighs,
A flicker emerges, where wonder complies.
With butterflies drifting on whispers of air,
Magic unveils in the world we both share.

Through the tapestry woven of stories untold,
Every thread shimmering, brilliant and bold.
We dance on the edge, where reality bends,
In flickers of moments, where bravery mends.

In the heart of the night, the stars twinkle bright,
Painting our futures with sparks of pure light.
As laughter unfurls, carrying tales from afar,
The flicker of fantasy guides us to star.

With courage beside us, we leap through the haze,
Exploring the pathways of whimsical ways.
Through the flicker of fantasy, hearts ignite,
Adventurers call in the depths of the night.

So hold on to dreams that beg to be bold,
Where magic awaits in a shimmer of gold.
At the flicker of fantasy's edge, come and see,
The wonders that blossom, forever wild and free.

Luminous Dreams Among the Glade

Beneath an arching sky, where starlight beams,
Luminous visions flow into our dreams.
Among ancient trees, bathed in silver glow,
The glade sings of magic, inviting us to flow.

Soft whispers arise, like petals that drift,
In the warmth of the night, as spirits uplift.
Each moment a treasure, so precious and sweet,
In luminous dreams, where heartbeats repeat.

The brook laughs and giggles, as it twirls on by,
Reflecting the secrets held deep in the sky.
With every flicker, beneath the moon's gleam,
We dance through the shadows, alive in our dream.

Together we wander, through glimmers and sighs,
With hope in our chests as we reach for the skies.
In luminous dreams among the darkened glade,
We weave our own stories, where memories fade.

So linger a moment, let the magic abound,
In luminous glimmers, our souls will be found.
With dreams ever shining, together we play,
In the heart of the glade, let our spirits sway.

Radiance in the Veil of Shadows

In twilight's hush, the whispers sing,
A light emerges from darkest spring.
With silken strands of silver spun,
The shadows dance, but dreams are won.

A flicker bright in solemn fate,
Guiding hearts to love innate.
The veil that shrouds our weary sight,
Can part, revealing hidden light.

In every corner, joy awaits,
Amidst the glimmer of fate's gates.
Through ember's glow and laughter loud,
We'll find the strength to stand unbowed.

The journey twists, the path unknown,
Yet in the dark, we find our home.
With every step, new hope set free,
A radiant dance beneath the tree.

The Flicker of Forgotten Wishes

In corners dim where wishes lay,
A flicker dims but will not stray.
The echoes of the dreams once cast,
Are sewn with threads of future's past.

With whispered words on softest breeze,
They rise and swirl through ancient trees.
With each sigh told, a shimmer stirs,
Returning to the heart that purrs.

Forgotten hopes in shadows creep,
Yet in the stillness, secrets keep.
A flicker born from heart's desire,
Will light the dark, set dreams afire.

Through tear-streaked paths and pieces lost,
We'll reach the heights despite the cost.
For each wish held, is worth the fight,
A beacon bright against the night.

Aetherial Glows from Sylvan Realms

In forests deep where wonders weave,
The aether glows, we dare believe.
With every breath, the magic flows,
In gentle whispers, life bestows.

The sylvan realms, a tapestry,
Of emerald dreams and mystery.
With flowers wild and shadows bold,
The tales of old are yet retold.

Amidst the boughs, the creatures play,
In dappled light, they find their way.
A world of wonder, softly spun,
Where every heart beats as one.

A glimmer bright in nature's hand,
Invites us close, to understand.
Through layers rich, the spirit grows,
In sylvan depths, the aether glows.

Echoes of Fire Beneath the Starlit Canopy

Beneath the stars, a fire gleams,
It echoes back our whispered dreams.
In night's embrace, we find our souls,
Like embers bright, we seek our goals.

The canopy of velvet dark,
Watches as we ignite the spark.
With flickering hearts, we gather round,
In unity, our hopes abound.

The flames will dance, the shadows sway,
As laughter rises with the day.
In every crackle, stories weave,
Of love and loss, of those who believe.

We sit as one, beneath the glow,
Our spirits high, the warmth we sow.
Through fire's light, we dare to dream,
And bask beneath the moonlit beam.

Flickers in the Twilight Grove

In shadows deep where whispers dwell,
The twilight grove casts its spell.
Soft petals sigh, as breezes sigh,
While fireflies twinkle in the sky.

A silver moon hangs low and bright,
Illuminating dreams of night.
The trees, they rustle with delight,
As stars awaken from their flight.

A pool of calm reflects the glow,
Of ancient tales that ebb and flow.
With every flicker, secrets prove,
The heart beats on in twilight grove.

In corners where the shadows play,
The echoes of the past convey,
A magic spun in threads so fine,
Where time stands still, and dreams entwine.

So venture forth, dear traveler bold,
Beneath the boughs of stories told.
In flickers bright, the night will weave,
A tapestry that none believe.

Whispers of the Woodland Flame

Through crackling leaves and velvet night,
The woodland flame ignites pure light.
With every flicker, tales ignite,
Of ancient woods and hearts so bright.

Whispers shared 'neath canopies wide,
Beneath the stars where dreams abide.
The winds entwine with secrets sung,
Where every soul feels forever young.

A dance of shadows, wild and free,
As fireflies twirl with harmony.
With ember's glow, they forge a path,
To realms of joy, beyond the wrath.

In flickering tongues, the forest speaks,
With gentle murmur that softly seeks.
Through boughs and brambles, hopes take flight,
In whispers shared beneath the night.

So linger here, where hearts may roam,
In woodland's flame, we find our home.
With open hearts, let magic reign,
In every spark, in every strain.

Ember Threads in Enchanted Air

In tangled woods where memories play,
The ember threads weave night and day.
A tapestry of dreams and fears,
Where laughter lingers, and joy appears.

The evening breeze, a wizard's charm,
Enfolds the world in soft alarm.
Each flicker glows, a promise kept,
A dance of hopes where shadows leapt.

Beneath the stars, unknown we tread,
With every step, where light is fed.
For with each spark, a secret stirs,
In enchanted air, the magic purrs.

The forest hums a lullaby,
As fleeting moments wander by.
On ember threads, our stories flow,
In every heart the fire will grow.

So take a breath, embrace the night,
In enchanted air, let spirits light.
With every ember, dreams align,
In threads of magic, souls entwine.

Dances of the Luminous Fae

In moonlit glades where fairies sway,
The luminous fae come out to play.
With laughter bright, and voices sweet,
They weave the night with twinkling feet.

Amidst the flowers, joy takes flight,
In shimmers soft, they greet the night.
With shimmering wings in silver streams,
They gather starlight, weave our dreams.

They twirl and spin in joyous tune,
Beneath the watchful eyes of moon.
An ancient dance, so wild and free,
In every whirl, we feel the glee.

In hidden nooks where shadows dwell,
The fae weave spells like magic spells.
With every step, enchantments kiss,
A moment lost in timeless bliss.

So join the revel, heed their call,
For laughter echoes through it all.
In dances bright, the night ignites,
With luminous fae to share our sights.

Secrets Woven in the Silver Light

In the quiet glade where shadows play,
Whispers of magic dance and sway,
Moonlight drapes a silken veil,
While secrets float on the nightingale.

Ancient trees with stories to tell,
Guarding the dreams where the faeries dwell,
Underneath the stars that gleam so bright,
Lies a world woven in silver light.

Softly the breeze carries hidden lore,
Echoes of enchantment from the forest floor,
Every leaf a tale, every branch a sigh,
In the hush of the dusk, where wishes fly.

Come, wanderer, tread on paths untraced,
With curiosity, let your heart be graced,
For in this realm, wonders ignite,
In the tapestry spun by the silver light.

So listen closely, let your spirit roam,
In the serene gloom, you'll find your home,
Where every glance reveals a new delight,
And dreams are whispered in the silver light.

Beneath the Canopy of Stardust

Beneath the canopy, where shadows blend,
And dreams unearth the magic they send,
Stardust glimmers on the cool night air,
Painting horizons with memories rare.

Glistening trails of light dance and sway,
Leading the lost on their starry way,
In the hush of the night, whispers unfold,
Stories of wishes and hearts made bold.

The owls call softly from branches high,
Echoing secrets in the pitch of the sky,
With every flutter, the night comes alive,
Where dreams and stardust together thrive.

Each twinkling star a path to explore,
Unlocking the treasures of legends of yore,
Beneath the vast dome, a heart takes flight,
In the embrace of the shimmering night.

So raise your eyes and let hope abide,
In the realm where the universe does confide,
For beneath this canopy so wide,
Lies a world of wonder, where dreams reside.

The Flickering Heart of the Forest

In the forest dense, where shadows play,
A flickering heart beats night and day,
With whispers of creatures that dwell in the dark,
Illuminating paths with a magical spark.

The fireflies twirl in a luminous dance,
Guiding the dreamers in a spellbound trance,
While the branches sway and the leaves softly sigh,
Inviting the wanderers drawing nigh.

An ancient oak stands with wisdom profound,
In every creak, deep history is found,
And hidden within its gnarled embrace,
Are memories of time and forgotten grace.

Listen, dear wanderer, to the forest's song,
A melody where every heart belongs,
In the flickering light, let your spirit soar,
And uncover the magic that hides at the core.

So venture forth with courage and glee,
Feel the pulse of enchantment, wild and free,
In the flickering heart, find your delight,
Where the forest's whispers blend with the light.

A Dream in the Whispering Woods

In the whispering woods where the shadows lean,
A dream takes flight, soft and unseen,
With every rustle, an echo of hope,
Guiding lost souls through the tangled scope.

The moon weaves silver through branches high,
As laughter dances on the breeze nearby,
In this haven of wonder, the heart finds its way,
To realms of enchantment where spirits play.

Each glade a canvas, painted with light,
Where wishes awaken and take their flight,
With the hush of the night, all wishes align,
In the heart of the woods, where magic enshrines.

So gather your dreams, let them softly unfurl,
In the whispering woods, let your heart twirl,
For here in this haven, under the starlit skies,
A dream waits beyond, where the wild magic lies.

So close your eyes, let the night draw you near,
To a world filled with wonders, sincere and clear,
In the whispering woods, let your spirit roam,
For a dream gently beckons, inviting you home.

Cavern of the Plumed Nightlight

In shadows deep where echoes sway,
The plumed nightlight starts to play,
Whispers of secrets, soft and low,
In the cavern's heart, the dreamers glow.

Beneath the arch of twinkling stars,
Time drifts on like distant bars,
The magic hums in every stone,
As if the night had gently grown.

With every breath, the stories weave,
Of lost adventures, hearts that grieve,
Yet here, in dark, a light is born,
From the very essence of the morn.

The flicker dances, a playful muse,
In depths where shadows gently fuse,
A haven found where spirits soar,
In this cavern, we dream once more.

The Hidden Flame of Woodland Spirits

In thickets dense, where sunlight fades,
A hidden flame through shadow wades,
The spirits murmur, low and clear,
Weaving their tales for all to hear.

Amongst the roots, a shimmer bright,
Beneath the boughs, they take to flight,
Bringing warmth to the chilly air,
Glimmers of laughter, softest care.

Their flickered dance paints leaves with gold,
In the woodland, stories unfold,
Every heartbeat, every sigh,
A sacred bond that will not die.

Around the blaze, the night ignites,
With lingering whispers of ancient rites,
For those who wander, lost and still,
Shall find their path, if they but will.

Enchantment Ignites Where Dreams Roam

In twilight's hush, where shadows blend,
With every breath, our dreams ascend,
A realm of wonder opens wide,
Where heart and soul in magic bide.

Stars align in patterns bright,
As dreams take wing in velvet night,
Whispers weave on silken threads,
Through echoes of the past that tread.

In every corner, a story lies,
Awakened by the moonlit skies,
In this sweet realm of the surreal,
Every heartbeat, love's appeal.

So let the enchantment overtake,
With every path that we shall make,
For where dreams roam, a spark will dance,
Igniting magic, given chance.

Celestial Glimmers in a Forest Heart

In the forest deep, where shadows play,
Celestial glimmers light the way,
Among the branches, soft and sleek,
The whispers of the night, unique.

Each twinkling light, a story spun,
Of ancients past, their battles won,
A tapestry of stars unfurls,
In nature's arms, the beauty swirls.

Through tangled paths, where secrets lie,
The forest breathes with a aching sigh,
Dreamers tread on mossy ground,
In every corner, magic found.

And as the night embraces soft,
We find our spirit, lifted, aloft,
In celestial glimmers, ever bright,
The forest's heart holds pure delight.

The Sparkling Dance of Mythic Beings

In twilight's hush, they weave and swirl,
With laughter light, in steps that twirl.
Beneath the stars, their shadows blend,
A merry chase that seems to bend.

With wings of silver, they take flight,
On dreams woven through the night.
Around the moon, their figures glide,
In realms where magic will abide.

Each flicker bright, a story spun,
Of battles fought, and races won.
In every sparkle, tales arise,
Of mythic beings and their skies.

So when the eve greets night with grace,
Look close to see their fleeting trace.
For within the dark, they dance and sing,
A secret joy that night can bring.

With whispers soft, in woodland glades,
The mythic beings charm like shades.
Together, they enchanting weave,
Their sparkling dance shall never leave.

Glowing Trails Through Ancient Woods

In ancient woods where secrets lie,
With twisted roots and a soft sigh.
The paths aglow with emerald light,
Guide wanderers through the night.

Each step reveals a whispered tale,
Of feral spirits that dare prevail.
Their laughter echoes through the trees,
As nightingales sing with the breeze.

With fireflies flickering like stars,
They lead us past the world's old scars.
Into the grove, where shadows play,
And myths breathe life in their own way.

There's magic here in every hue,
In shades of green and silver blue.
The ancient woods will keep their spell,
With glowing trails where stories dwell.

So walk this path, let wonder rise,
In every corner, a sweet surprise.
Through ancient woods, let your heart soar,
For magic waits behind each door.

Mystic Flare in the Silvan Night

In silvan night, the stars alight,
With mystic flares, a wondrous sight.
They dance upon the velvet skies,
While whispers weave in soft replies.

The owls do speak with ancient tongue,
And songs of old are sweetly sung.
Beneath the trees, the shadows creep,
In hallowed places where dreams sleep.

With every pulse of shimmering light,
The night unveils its secret might.
Elusive forms flit through the dark,
With every flicker, they leave a mark.

Echoes of laughter chase the gloom,
In each corner, the night finds room.
To let the magic gently spill,
And hold our hearts against the chill.

So find the flare in the silvan sky,
A spark of wonder as you fly.
For in the night, with every spark,
The world is stitched from light and dark.

Shadows Play with Glimpse of Radiance

Where shadows dance in fleeting haze,
They find their joy in twilight's grace.
A glimpse of radiance infuses night,
That flickers and fades, a joyous light.

With twinkling dust that softly glows,
They weave their tales where no one goes.
In moonlit glades, they charm and tease,
Riding on whispers from the breeze.

Each moment twirls in gentle sway,
As shadows play and dreams will stray.
To gather tales from eons past,
And slip away ere dawn is cast.

The laughter spills, a welcome sound,
In hidden realms where time is unbound.
While branches sway, a veil is drawn,
Where shadows dance until the dawn.

So when you glimpse that fleeting spark,
Know magic calls from realms so dark.
With shadows playing, don't take flight,
Stay close to glimpse the sweet delight.

The Unseen Tides of Ethereal Fire

In shadows cast by flickering light,
Soft whispers dance through the night sky,
Waves of warmth in a spectral flight,
Beyond the reach where dreamers lie.

With every glow, a secret's song,
The heart of night takes gentle breath,
In unseen tides where we belong,
Entwined with life, unbound by death.

A flicker bright through darkened haze,
Unlocking realms with silent grace,
Ethereal embers weave their maze,
Into the void, we softly chase.

Here lies a spark, a moment's thrill,
The warmth of fire in tender air,
With each heartbeat, our dreams fulfill,
As magic flows, we chip despair.

Beneath the stars, we still remain,
In whispers shared, our souls take flight,
The unseen tides shall call our name,
Forever drawn to ethereal light.

Murmurs in the Glow of Elder Trees

Beneath their boughs, a world unfolds,
Where secrets blend with ancient bark,
Murmurs hidden, softly told,
And shadows play in twilight's dark.

The leaves hum low with tales of yore,
Of wisdom found in whispered breath,
As roots stretch deep to search for more,
Connecting hearts beyond all death.

In glimmers soft, the fireflies gleam,
They twirl and dance in silver light,
Among the trees, we chase a dream,
In echoes sweet, we find our sight.

With every turn, the night unfolds,
A symphony of life at play,
As elder trees guard all they hold,
In twilight's glow, we lose delay.

Stand still, breathe in the earth's soft grace,
With each entwined branch, we find our way,
In murmurs sweet, we seek a place,
Where time stands still, and hearts can sway.

Serene Ripples of Twilight Radiance

In shades of dusk, the world awakes,
With ripples dancing on the stream,
As twilight's breath the silence takes,
A moment caught within a dream.

The moon, a pearl in velvet sky,
Reflects the calm upon the shore,
Where whispers weave and spirits fly,
In serene rhythms, forevermore.

Each glimmer shines, a fleeting glance,
Awakening joys from deep within,
In twilight's hush, we chance a dance,
Where every loss can turn to win.

The stars emerge, like scattered seeds,
Each one a hope, a touch of fate,
In quiet pools, the heart still leads,
A dance of light we celebrate.

Beneath the arch of starlit grace,
The ripples spread, our spirits soar,
In twilight's glow, we find our place,
A serenade forevermore.

Fragments of Magic Within Nature's Grasp

Among the ferns and dewy blades,
A spark ignites, a whisper clear,
In nature's fold, where magic fades,
We find the tales that hearts hold dear.

The rustling leaves, a gentle sigh,
As critters hop from root to root,
While soft winds weave the evening's cry,
In every sound, a wondrous truth.

The shadows stretch, the day departs,
A flicker here, a glow appears,
In fragments shared, we weave our arts,
And plant the seeds of joyful years.

With every breeze that stirs the night,
A promise made, a fate aligned,
In nature's grasp, our dreams take flight,
In every breath, our souls entwined.

So linger here, let magic dwell,
Among the roots where stories run,
In nature's heart, we'll weave a spell,
Forever basking in the sun.

The Glow of the Wandering Wind

In twilight's hush the whispers play,
The wandering wind calls out my name.
It dances through the leaves' soft sway,
A flicker of light, a fleeting flame.

Each breath it takes, the darkness breaks,
A melody of old that stirs the soul.
Its gentle touch, the heart awakes,
A promise sung, to make us whole.

Through valleys deep, where shadows creep,
It wanders forth with secrets to share.
Through roots it weaves, where dreams may sleep,
A fleeting spark, a breath of air.

The glimmer bright as starlight gleams,
Ignites the path where hope resides.
In every gust, the magic streams,
With every gust, the world abides.

So follow close, the wind's sweet song,
Let every note be a guide anew.
In whispered tales where we belong,
The glow will shine, forever true.

Splintered Light in the Heart of Night

When shadows gather, fears take flight,
A splintered light begins to glow.
It pierces through the cloak of night,
A beacon for the brave to know.

In quiet corners, secrets hum,
The heart beats loud, a haunting drum.
By candle's flicker, dreams will come,
The warmth within, not left to numb.

Through starlit skies, the echoes dart,
Where whispered hopes may yet collide.
In every sigh, we find our part,
As night unveils what we can't hide.

From silken threads of silver spun,
We weave our tales from dusk to dawn.
With splintered light, the world begun,
In every heart, the magic yawns.

So fear not night when shadows play,
For glimmers wait to light the way.
In every breath, find courage stay,
And let the splintered light convey.

Flickering Byways of Dream and Myth

In realms of dreams where starlight weaves,
A tapestry of whispered sighs.
Through flickering byways, the heart believes,
In shadowed trails where magic lies.

Echoes call from ancient lore,
With wondrous tales in twilight's glow.
As myths entwine on the sandy shore,
In twilight hues, the stories flow.

Through moonlit paths, the fables spin,
Each ember bright, a memory's gleam.
In every heart, the hope within,
As fleeting moments build a dream.

A glimmer caught in laughter's tune,
As wild as night, as pure as day.
With every step beneath the moon,
We find our joy in child's play.

So wander forth, through dream's embrace,
Let myths reveal what we believe.
In every flicker, a sacred space,
Where dreams converge, and hearts retrieve.

A Glimpse of Magic's Breath

In quiet woods where echoes sigh,
A glimpse of magic stirs the air.
With every breeze, a lullaby,
To weave a spell beyond compare.

The world holds secrets, soft and sweet,
In hidden paths where wonders bloom.
With whispered winds, our spirits meet,
In every shade, a ghostly loom.

Through sunlight's dance, the shadows play,
As magic's breath entwines the trees.
In every rustle, dreams will sway,
Like gentle waves upon the breeze.

With every sigh the heart can find,
A thread of light amidst the night.
In every pulse, a love untwined,
In every spark, a world of flight.

So breathe in deep, the magic's call,
Let every moment linger near.
For in each breath, we rise and fall,
And find our truth, where hearts are clear.

Shards of Light Beneath the Canopy

In the quiet woods, where shadows dwell,
Shards of light through branches swell.
Dancing whispers, tales untold,
Nature's secrets, soft and bold.

A rustle here, a flicker there,
Magic lingers in the air.
Woven dreams of earth and sky,
Beneath the canopy, spirits fly.

Crickets sing their nightly song,
While wandering starlings dart along.
Twilight paints the world anew,
In hues of gold and gentle blue.

The leaves above, they softly sway,
Guiding wanderers on their way.
Through shimmering paths, the heart takes flight,
Chasing shadows, seeking light.

In this realm where wonders gleam,
Reality bends, and truths redeem.
So tread with care, dear seeker bright,
For magic thrives in shards of light.

Glimmers of Mischief in Moonlit Mist

In the twilight hour, where shadows creep,
Glimmers of mischief begin to leap.
Moonlight dances on leaves so green,
Stirring secrets, unseen, serene.

A playful spirit tugs at the night,
Twinkling stars, a charming sight.
Echoes of laughter fill the glade,
Caught in the charm of a playful cascade.

With every rustle, a story unfolds,
Of mischievous sprites and tales bold.
They twirl and spin, in a whirl of glee,
In moonlit mist, wild and free.

Beware the paths where shadows loom,
For they guard laughter and potential doom.
Chasing the night, with hearts so light,
Glimmers of mischief take to flight.

So heed the call of the whimsy's kiss,
In the darkened woods, you'll find your bliss.
For when the moon smiles, spirits play,
In glimmers of mischief, chase the day.

Secret Fireflies in the Fairy Glade

In the depths of night, where dreams abide,
Secret fireflies in whispers glide.
They flicker soft, like stars set free,
Guiding the lost, a luminous spree.

In a glade where fairies weave,
Magic blooms, you just believe.
Petals shimmer, and shadows dance,
Inviting souls into a trance.

With every glow, a tale awakes,
Of ancient woods and the paths it takes.
Secrets shared in the flitting light,
Lost to time, but shining bright.

Hold your breath and make a wish,
As fireflies leap with a gentle swish.
Among the flowers, softness flows,
In the fairy glade, where wonder grows.

So seek the glow where twilight meets,
And let the magic guide your feet.
For secret fireflies dream and play,
In hidden corners, night turns to day.

Twists of Fate Among the Starry Boughs

Underneath the sprawling trees,
Twists of fate dance on the breeze.
Branching paths beneath the night,
Whispers echo, soft and light.

Stars align in patterns strange,
Life's odd turns, a lovely change.
Each choice leads to bright unknowns,
Fate weaves tales in whispered tones.

As shadows weave through ancient roots,
Silent prayers take subtle shoots.
Among the boughs, the dreams take form,
In every heart, a quiet storm.

Come tread with care, the night is young,
In the silence, the songs are sung.
Fortune smiles on those who dare,
Among the starry boughs, magic's rare.

So gaze above, let your heart take flight,
In twists of fate, embrace the night.
For every star holds a promise deep,
In the woods where secrets sleep.

Fables of Flame and Glade

In the heart of the glade, a flicker does dance,
Secrets in shadows, a mystical chance.
Flames whisper stories of old in the night,
Binding the forest in warm, glowing light.

Roaming the pathways, the will-o'-the-wisps,
Guide weary travelers with flickering lips.
Crowned in the dusk, the tall trees stand proud,
Guardians of tales that echoes aloud.

A tapestry woven with threads of the past,
Each ember a memory, a spell that's cast.
Nature's own fables of laughter and tears,
Lifted by breezes that soften our fears.

Footsteps in silence, a presence we feel,
The warmth of the hearth, a soft, tender reel.
In the glade's embrace, where the wild things play,
The flame's tender flicker will never decay.

So gather your stories, your dreams, and your lore,
For time in the glade opens every door.
Here fables of flame wrap us in their glow,
A magic that lingers, eternal and slow.

Serenade of the Mysterious Glimmer

Beneath the veil of a starlit expanse,
Glimmers arise in a delicate dance.
Whispers of night wind through the tall grass,
Carrying secrets that only we pass.

With each gentle flicker, a story unfolds,
Of love and of loss, of brave hearts and bold.
A serenade summoned from shadows so deep,
Awakens the wonders that lie in our sleep.

Moonbeams paint silver on faces aglow,
As spirits of twilight begin to bestow.
Their presence surrounds in a mystical haze,
Filling the night with enchanting displays.

Together we wander, hand in warm hand,
Through echoes of magic in this timeless land.
The glimmering stars, our companions so bright,
Guide us through paths of shimmering light.

So sing to the night, let your heart take flight,
In the serenade woven from dark into light.
Each glimmer a promise, a wish softly made,
Forever embraced in the night's sweet cascade.

Mystical Glades and Enchanted Nights

When twilight descends and the sky turns to gold,
The glades come alive, with their stories retold.
Each whispering leaf is a note in the air,
Binding the night with enchantments so rare.

In the depths of the forest, where shadows do creep,
Magic awakens, and mysteries seep.
The moonlight like silver drapes over the trees,
A cloak of the night that sways with the breeze.

Fantastical creatures weave in and out,
Playing their games, with a soft, merry shout.
Hiding in whispers, they watch and they wait,
Inviting us closer, enthralling our fate.

The stars share their secrets to those who believe,
Unfolding the wonders that nature can weave.
With each breath we take, in this enchanted embrace,
We find our true selves, lost in time and space.

So let us discover the night's tender glow,
In mystical glades where the wild breezes flow.
Together we'll dance, 'neath the starlit delight,
Awakening dreams in the enchanted night.

Echoes of Twilight's Heartbeat

Twilight descends, painting skies with its brush,
A heartbeat of evening, the world starts to hush.
Echoes resound through the cool, gentle air,
Whispers of magic, a moment to share.

In the realm of the dusk where the shadows entwine,
Every flicker of light seems perfectly aligned.
Creatures awaken, from slumber they rise,
Revealing the secrets kept hidden from eyes.

Time drips like honey, sweet moments we hold,
Stories of wonder within us unfold.
The heartbeat of twilight, a soothing refrain,
Wraps 'round our spirits, igniting the plain.

With each gentle sigh of the breeze through the leaves,
The night weaves its magic, as nature believes.
In echoes resounding, our hopes take their flight,
Carried on whispers through the blanket of night.

So gather the echoes, the dreams that ignite,
For twilight's soft heartbeat guides all into light.
Together we'll stand, as the day turns to dark,
Embraced by the magic, ignited by spark.

A Dance of Glimmers in the Mist

In the glade where shadows play,
Whispers echo, come what may.
Glimmers tease the fading light,
As night unfolds her shrouded flight.

Waves of silver, soft and rare,
Sway with secrets in the air.
Leaves entwine in playful glee,
Enchantments stir, wild and free.

Hushed are all the woodland calls,
Each small breeze a tale recalls.
Glimmers flicker, dance, and spin,
Inviting hearts, the night begins.

With every spark, a promise made,
In twilight's grip, dreams won't fade.
Beneath the stars that twinkle bright,
Magic blooms in the tender night.

So join the dance, release your sigh,
Where glimmers whisper and hopes fly.
In the mist, let spirits soar,
And dance till dawn, forever more.

Beneath the Fabled Night Sky

Beneath the stars, a tale unfolds,
Of ancient dreams and courage bold.
The moon, a guardian high above,
Watches o'er the world with love.

Mysterious night, with wonders rare,
Keeps its secrets in the air.
Each twinkling star, a story spun,
Whispers soft, the night's begun.

Through shimmering veils of mystic glow,
The midnight breeze begins to flow.
Echoes of laughter, faint and sweet,
As shadows dance on silken feet.

A tapestry of dark and light,
Embraces all within its height.
With moonbeams kissing every tree,
The world transforms in mystery.

So breathe the magic, let it rise,
As dreams take flight 'neath fabled skies.
In this vast expanse, we remain,
Chasing echoes and gentle rain.

Flickering Hopes in the Moonlight

In the hour when shadows blend,
Flickers of hope begin to mend.
Moonlit paths, a guiding thread,
Illuminating dreams unsaid.

Every glimmer speaks a truth,
Carving tales from whispered youth.
Stars alight with tales anew,
As distant hearts begin to brew.

Softly calling, a gentle hum,
Inviting all to join the fun.
Through silver streams, our souls entwine,
In moonlit joy, forever shine.

With every step, beneath the glow,
The heart finds peace, as hopes bestow.
Whispers weave in night's embrace,
Every flicker a sacred space.

So let us dance on moonlit floors,
With flickering hopes, we'll open doors.
In this realm of dreamy light,
Our spirits soar, in endless flight.

Ethereal Secrets of the Woodland

In the heart of the ancient grove,
Ethereal secrets softly strove.
Muffled whispers of tales untold,
Guarded closely, treasure gold.

The sway of branches, a subtle song,
Echoes of the woodlands strong.
Every leaf, a story spun,
Unraveled at the rise of sun.

Mystical creatures roam the night,
Bathed in moonbeams, shining bright.
With every rustle, hopes take flight,
Under the watch of the silver light.

Frogs in chorus, owls arrange,
The symphony of night, so strange.
In twilight's love, they weave and play,
Ethereal secrets, come what may.

So wander deep where shadows dwell,
Within the woods, their magic swell.
In the embrace of tree and flower,
Discover life in every hour.

Secrets Awakened in the Whispered Wind

In twilight's breathe, a promise glows,
Soft secrets linger where the wild rose grows.
The wind carries tales from ages past,
While shadows play, their silence cast.

Each rustle tells of dreams anew,
In the heart of night, the stars shine through.
A gentle murmur, a beckoning call,
Awakening wonders that beyond us sprawl.

Whispers float on the softest breeze,
Curious echoes among the trees.
In the quiet, the world unfolds,
As ancient mysteries begin to be told.

With every sigh, the forest breathes,
In magic's grasp, the heart believes.
The wind's embrace, a lover's tune,
Beneath the watchful eye of the moon.

Secrets awaken, their veils now shed,
In the hidden paths where few dare tread.
Listen closely, for there you'll find,
The gentle whispers of the gentle wind.

Dreamlight Dancing on Woodland Floor

In the hush of night, the fairies play,
Dreamlight glimmers, chasing shadows away.
A tapestry woven with silver thread,
Where imagination and wonder are fed.

Among the trees, a soft melody sings,
The woodland floor, where enchantment clings.
With every flutter, the starlight beams,
Casting spells in the heart of dreams.

Glimmers of magic in every stride,
Where the gentle fawns and the whispers reside.
Each heartbeat echoes a rhythmic score,
As dawn's first blush peeks through the door.

The leaves rustle with a lover's sigh,
As daylight dances in the azure sky.
In quiet moments, when time stands still,
The woodland comes alive with thrill.

Dreamlight dances, a swirling embrace,
With nature's pulse, a warm, tender grace.
Each spark ignites the fervor within,
In the heart of the woods, let dreams begin.

Mysteries of the Heralded Night

In the cloak of darkness, wonders thrive,
The mysteries whisper, keeping dreams alive.
Echoes of laughter through branches hum,
As secrets gather, the night has come.

Beneath the cloak of the starlit veil,
Each shadow reveals a forgotten tale.
A moonlit guide through the winding paths,
Where time unwinds in the night's gentle baths.

Awake, the owls sing their refrains,
As gentle breezes lift the remains.
With every flicker of candlelight,
The heart pulses with delight.

The forest breathes, a sigh so deep,
In quiet rhythms, the world's secrets keep.
Each rustling leaf, a whispered grace,
A fleeting glance at time and space.

In the depth of night, we seek and find,
The stories woven, threads of the mind.
Let the mysteries serve as our guide,
As shadows dance on fate's secret tide.

The Radiance of Whispered Wishes

In twilight's glow, dreams start to bloom,
With every star, a wish finds room.
Softly they whisper, carried by night,
As hearts ignite in tender light.

Whispers of hope in the silken air,
Float through the gardens, both subtle and rare.
With every flicker, a longing sigh,
In the quiet moments, our spirits fly.

As moonbeams dance on the water's face,
The radiance unfolds, a luminous grace.
Each shimmering light a promise made,
In the tapestry of dreams displayed.

With wishes gathered, our hearts align,
Among the twinkling, the stars define.
In the stillness, our longing thrums,
While destiny whispers, sweetly it hums.

The night paints colors, so vivid, so bright,
In the world of dreams where wishes take flight.
Let the radiance guide us, come what may,
In the heart of the night, our dreams shall stay.

Enchanted Flickers Beneath the Stars

In the quiet night, dreams take flight,
A tapestry woven of soft starlight.
Whispers of magic dance in the air,
While shadows of secrets linger with care.

Beneath the moon's glow, the fairies twine,
Casting their wishes on paths so divine.
Each flicker a promise, a tale yet untold,
Where hearts are enchanted, and wonders unfold.

The nightingale sings to the slumbering trees,
As breezes weave stories with delicate ease.
Beneath twinkling skies, all worries take flight,
Embraced in the warmth of magical night.

Stars shimmer softly, like whispers of fate,
Guiding lost souls through the night, so sedate.
In the embrace of the dark, we are free,
To dream of enchantments, as vast as the sea.

So linger awhile, in this mystical hue,
For beneath the starlight, all things can renew.
With each enchanted flicker, let wonder resume,
For magic awaits in the heart of the gloom.

Sirens of Ember and Enchantment

In the heart of the forest, where shadows entwine,
Whispers of sirens weave tales divine.
With flames that flicker like laughter on lips,
They dance in the moonlight, a world in eclipse.

Their voices cascade like a melodious stream,
Enticing the dreamers, igniting their dream.
Underneath canopies woven with light,
The air sparkles golden, in the hush of the night.

Each ember a story, each glow a delight,
A symphony plays with the stars as its sight.
The call of the sirens, both tender and bold,
Awakens the spirit, like legends of old.

Through glades draped in mystery, echoes will sound,
Where tales of enchantment and freedom abound.
Woven with magic, the night offers bliss,
In the arms of the sirens, it's hard to resist.

So listen intently to the songs of the night,
For within every note, lies a flicker of light.
Embrace the enchantment, let yourself roam,
For the sirens await, calling you home.

Secrets of the Starlit Grove

In the starlit grove, where the shadows play,
Secrets are hidden beneath branches that sway.
Ancient trees whisper their tales to the night,
Guardians of dreams, wrapped in silver light.

Each leaf holds a longing, each breeze carries song,
The heartbeat of magic, where we all belong.
With fireflies twinkling in jubilant glee,
The grove pulses softly, alive and carefree.

Moonlight spills gently like silk on the ground,
Awakening wonders and whispers profound.
In the quiet embrace of the everwood shade,
Lies a tapestry woven that time cannot fade.

Entwined in the secrets, our spirits take flight,
As guardians watch and guide through the night.
With each step we wander, each heartbeat we share,
In the starlit grove, we shall always find care.

So linger, dear dreamer, beneath the wide skies,
For the secrets of magic await your wise eyes.
In the cradle of night, let your worries dissolve,
In the starlit grove, let your heart find absolve.

Fireflies Beneath the Ancient Oak

Beneath the ancient oak, where shadows dwell,
Fireflies twinkle, casting their spell.
In the hush of the evening, they whisper and glide,
Like memories flickering on the swift night tide.

Their dance spins a web of shimmering light,
Creating a haven in the embrace of night.
With each gentle flutter, they awaken delight,
A chorus of wonders takes wing in the light.

The oak stands as keeper of stories untold,
It cradles the dreams and the secrets of old.
Under its branches, where time holds its breath,
We find comfort and warmth that transcends even death.

As dusk wraps the world in its silken embrace,
The fireflies gather, a sparkling race.
In their radiant dance, they weave solace and cheer,
Beneath the old oak, where magic draws near.

So pause in this moment, let your spirit ignite,
As fireflies guide you through the velvety night.
For beneath the great oak, where dreams intertwine,
Lies a treasure of magic, eternally divine.

The Dance of the Celestial Fireflies

In twilight's glow, the fireflies wend,
With whispers soft, their glow they send.
Like tiny stars that kiss the night,
They twirl and sway in joyful flight.

A ballet bright in moonlit air,
Where every heart can pause and stare.
Their dances weave through branches high,
A luminous dream in the dusky sky.

With laughter light, they spin and twine,
Each flicker a secret, each gleam divine.
In this enchanted waltz they play,
An ode to night that steals away.

In shadows deep, where wishes wake,
They flutter softly for hope's own sake.
Each twinkle tells a tale of yore,
Of magic found and lost before.

And as the dawn begins to break,
The fireflies whisper, "Awake, awake!"
Their dance may end, but in our hearts,
The memories linger, never depart.

Echoing Glimmer in Hidden Valleys

In valleys deep where silence dwells,
A glimmer glows, a story tells.
The echoes tumble, soft and low,
Of secrets buried long ago.

Amidst the mist, a light appears,
A spark of hope that calms our fears.
It beckons gently from afar,
A guiding touch, a distant star.

The shadows dance, the branches sway,
As whispers guide us on our way.
Each glint and gleam a step anew,
Through hidden paths, where dreams come true.

With every step, the glimmer grows,
A thread of magic, soft it flows.
In every corner, every bend,
The light unveils the heart's true mend.

So let us wander, hand in hand,
Through whispering woods, through golden sand.
In valleys deep, let truth be found,
For in the echoes, joy resounds.

The Lure of the Enchanted Flame

Upon the hearth, the fire burns bright,
An ember's glow, a warm delight.
With crackling whispers, tales unfold,
Of brave hearts true and treasures bold.

The flames leap high, they twist and turn,
In every flicker, passions burn.
They draw us close, like moths to light,
Their dance a spell that feels so right.

With shadows cast on walls so wide,
We find ourselves, our dreams collide.
Each blaze a beacon, guiding home,
Beneath the spell, we're free to roam.

A warmth that wraps like tender arms,
With stories woven through its charms.
It tells of love, of loss, of fate,
A magical bond we celebrate.

So gather 'round, let laughter rise,
As tales ignite under starlit skies.
For within this flame, our spirits soar,
An enchanted lure forevermore.

Fables Flickering in the Darkness

When night enfolds the world in black,
Fables whisper from the cracks.
With flickers soft, stories emerge,
Of distant lands and dreams that surge.

In every shadow, a tale resides,
In whispered winds, the truth abides.
With courage drawn from stars above,
The heart ignites, it dances of love.

The darkness holds a gentle weight,
As fables weave through time and fate.
Each tale a thread, each thread a song,
They guide us right when things go wrong.

Through ancient woods and silver streams,
We chase the echoes of our dreams.
In flickering lights, we find our way,
Each fable blooms, become our stay.

So close your eyes and hear the call,
Let ancient words enchant us all.
For in the dark, where shadows play,
Fables flicker, lighting our way.

Dappled Light Among the Ancient Trees

Whispers of leaves in golden hue,
Dancing shadows play their game,
Sunbeams filter, soft and true,
Nature's beauty, never the same.

Roots entwined in emerald earth,
Stories etched in gnarled bark,
Each ring a tale of silent worth,
A testament to seasons dark.

Birdsongs weave through sunlit glades,
As squirrels scamper, swift and bold,
In leafy halls where time parades,
The mysteries of the woods unfold.

In this haven, spirits roam,
The ancient trees their watchful gaze,
In dappled light, they find their home,
A sanctuary through the haze.

So wander here, let worries cease,
Amongst the giants, wise and free,
In every rustle, find your peace,
Dappled light among the trees.

Glowing Tales of Forgotten Spirits

In the shadows where silence dwells,
Tales of wraiths are softly spun,
Echoes rise like whispered bells,
Lost at dawn, when night is done.

Wanderers tread on haunted ground,
Where secrets linger in the dark,
With gentle sighs and dreams unbound,
They leave behind a faded mark.

Glowing lights in the midnight air,
Flicker gently, spirits dance,
Stories told beyond compare,
Inviting all to take a chance.

In moonlit groves, their shadows blend,
With hopes and fears that time forgot,
A timeless waltz around the bend,
In every heart, a sacred spot.

So linger softly, heed their call,
For glowing tales of those who've passed,
In that quiet, enchanted thrall,
Their gentle wisdom holds us fast.

Woven Threads of Celestial Light

In midnight skies where dreams take flight,
Stars are woven, bright and bold,
Threads of silver, pure delight,
Each twinkle tells a tale untold.

Galaxies swirl in cosmic dance,
Veils of magic, softly spun,
With every glance, we find romance,
In the tapestry of the sun.

Constellations share their lore,
Of heroes, myths, and worlds unseen,
Each sparkling gem, a beckoned door,
To realms of wonder, wild and green.

Eclipsed by time, yet brightly shine,
A whisper hints of what may come,
In this vast, celestial design,
The heartbeat of the universe hums.

So look above, let spirit soar,
In woven threads of endless night,
For in each star, a dream to explore,
A glimpse of hope, a spark of light.

Beneath the Veil of Stardust

Beneath the sky, where secrets sleep,
And starlit dreams in silence shine,
The universe its watch shall keep,
With every wish, a thread divine.

Veils of stardust softly fall,
A sprinkle of the cosmos' grace,
In every grain, the heavens call,
Invoking wonder, time, and space.

Ghosts of comets streak the night,
In pathways drawn from history's hand,
In their wake, they spark the light,
Of legends lost in cosmic sand.

So pause, dear soul, beneath this dome,
And let the magic fill your heart,
For in the vastness, we find home,
Each heartbeat a celestial part.

In whispers soft, the stars implore,
To dream of worlds beyond our sight,
Beneath the veil, we seek for more,
Forever drawn to starlit night.

Songs of Shadows and Starlight

In the whispering woods, where shadows play,
The secrets of night dance in silvered sway.
Beneath the great trees, the spirits sing,
A lullaby soft as the hush of spring.

Stars shimmer like jewels in the velvety dark,
Winking and nodding, each one a spark.
Glimmers of laughter, in the cool, crisp air,
Echo the tales that are woven with care.

Moonlight spills softly on the dew-kissed grass,
While time drifts away like the clouds that pass.
In this enchanted realm, dreams take their flight,
Carried on breezes both gentle and light.

So linger a while, let the magic unfold,
For stories of starlight are waiting to be told.
Find solace in shadows where wonders reside,
And dance with the night, as the world opens wide.

Each moment a thread in the fabric of night,
Where shadows and starlight embrace with delight.
Breathe in the silence, let go of the woes,
For the heart of the night is where true magic flows.

Between Reality and Folklore

When twilight weaves tales from the fabric of dreams,
And shadows stretch long under moon's silver beams,
In the realm between worlds, where stories entwine,
Legends are born on the edge of divine.

With flickering lanterns that guide wandering souls,
Through brambles of fate where enchantment unfolds,
Each whisper a promise of wonders untold,
In the embrace of the night, mysteries unfold.

Glimpses of giants that roam through the mist,
Fairies that sparkle in moonlight's soft kiss,
They dance on the borders of what we believe,
In the folds of the night, it's magic we weave.

With echoes of laughter that float through the air,
In the space between reality, free from despair,
Here, time is a river that flows to the past,
Connecting our hearts to the shadows at last.

So listen closely, let your spirit take flight,
For between reality and folklore's soft light,
The whispers of ages beckon you near,
To a world woven richly with stories we hear.

The Ascendant Glow of Myth

When dawn heralds dreams with its golden embrace,
And myths are reborn in the sun's radiant face.
The essence of legends ignites the new day,
In the glow of the sun, old stories replay.

With heroes ignited by flames of the past,
Their journeys unfurling in shadows they cast.
In timeless reflections, let truth intertwine,
For the heart of each myth is its essence divine.

Galaxies pivot on the axis of lore,
Where whispers of ancients emerge from the core.
Each heartbeat, a chorus, each breath, a refrain,
A symphony sung through joy, sorrow, and pain.

So gather the tales of the ones who have bled,
For every great myth was beautifully bred.
As the sky blushes bright, let your spirit take flight,
In the ascendant glow, find your truth in the light.

In this tapestry rich with the colors of soul,
The ascendant glow of myth makes us whole.
Hold close to the stories, let them resonate,
For in every old tale lies a door to our fate.

Echoes of a Celestial Glow

When the night sky awakens with stars shining bright,
And the moon casts its glow on the dreams of the night,
Listen intently to the shadows that speak,
For echoes of stories weave whispers antique.

With each pulse of starlight, the heavens align,
Tales written in constellations, divine.
Navigating the cosmos, our spirits take flight,
Igniting the darkness with fragments of light.

In the silence of night, where mysteries dwell,
Each whisper of stardust, a flicker, a spell.
The magic of moments that lift us to soar,
In echoes of wonder, we yearn for much more.

So pause, in the stillness, embrace the unknown,
For the universe beckons us to its throne.
In the dance of the cosmos, our hearts will align,
With the echoes of stars, let your spirit be fine.

As dawn gently tiptoes, dispelling the glow,
Remember the stories the night held in tow,
For echoes do linger, in shadows that flow,
And the celestial chorus will never let go.

Celestial Glimmers in a Hidden Grove

In a grove where shadows play,
Stars spill secrets, night turns day.
Whispers dance on twilight's sigh,
Beneath the moon, the fireflies fly.

Ancient trees in silence stand,
Guardians of this mystic land.
Laughter echoes, soft and clear,
As dreams awaken, drawing near.

Time stands still, the world in trance,
Nature's magic leads the dance.
Twinkling lights in leafy veils,
Spin enchanting, woven tales.

Hidden paths in silver glow,
Where forgotten rivers flow.
In the hush, a haunting tune,
Calls forth the heart beneath the moon.

All who wander, heed the call,
Let go of worries, rise and fall.
In this grove, let spirits soar,
As celestial glimmers prompt encore.

The Light of Lost Dreams

In corners dark, where shadows creep,
Lie hidden hopes, in silence deep.
Flickering lights, like distant stars,
Guide hearts through nights with endless scars.

Each shattered wish and whispered sigh,
Breathe life anew with dusk's soft cry.
Though dreams may fade, their echoes stay,
Illuminating paths, they'll find their way.

With every tear, a flicker shines,
Dancing through time, in tangled lines.
For lost dreams seek their rightful place,
In the embrace of time's warm grace.

So raise your eyes, let spirits mend,
For every loss can still transcend.
In the heart where light persists,
Lost dreams awaken, they still exist.

At dawn's first blush, they softly gleam,
Painting skies in hues of dream.
The light of lost dreams, ever bright,
Guides weary souls through endless night.

Flashes of Silver in the Verdant Abyss

In the depths where emeralds lie,
Silver sparks light the darkened sky.
Echoes whisper through the leaves,
Nature's bounty, it conceives.

Flashes bright, like shooting stars,
Paint the night with silver scars.
Each gleam a part of tales untold,
In verdant arms, the world unfolds.

Winding paths through shadows roam,
Calling forth the heart to home.
In the abyss, where wonders dwell,
Every flash, a hidden spell.

With every turn, a secret found,
In nature's breath, where dreams are bound.
So hold each shimmer, breathe it in,
In the dark, let the dance begin.

For in the depths of every night,
Silver flashes birth the light.
And through the verdant, vast expanse,
We venture forth, we take the chance.

Mystical Trails of Enchanted Light

Beneath the boughs where shadows weave,
Mystical trails, they interleave.
Guiding souls through time and space,
In this realm, we find our grace.

Each step a secret, softly shared,
In the magic, none be scared.
Glowing paths of soft delight,
Lead us deeper into night.

Whispers linger on the breeze,
Voices speaking through the trees.
In every glow, a promise made,
In the twilight, fears will fade.

With every twinkle, joy resounds,
A tapestry of dreams surrounds.
Together here, we take our flight,
On mystical trails of enchanted light.

Let hearts be open, wild and free,
For within the grove, we all can see.
That in this dance, with wonder bright,
We find our way through endless night.

Whimsy in the Glimmering Shadows

In the dappled light of dusk,
The shadows dance and sway,
Whispers weave through boughs and leaves,
In the twilight's soft array.

Curious sprites on gossamer wings,
Flit between the trees,
Chasing dreams and fleeting hopes,
In a symphony of breeze.

Moonbeams trace the winding paths,
Casting a silver hue,
Mysteries in the air abound,
For the bold and the true.

With each step, a tale unfolds,
Amongst the glimmering sights,
Boundless wonders wait to greet,
Those who seek the night.

Embrace the magic in the dark,
Let laughter fill the air,
For within the glimmering shadows,
Whimsy is everywhere.

Fragments of Luminescent Wishes

In the silence of the night,
Stars hang like silver threads,
Whispered wishes drift afar,
On the breeze where hope treads.

Each sigh a promise, softly spun,
In the tapestry of dreams,
Caught amongst the vibrant hues,
Of the moon's enchanting beams.

Luminous echoes shape the air,
Bright as the candles' glow,
Flickering softly, heart to heart,
In the twilight's gentle flow.

As fragments of wishes take their flight,
Across the velvet sky,
A shimmering chorus sings aloud,
To the stars that dance up high.

Hold tight to each spark of light,
For they hold stories dear,
In fragments of luminescent dreams,
That linger year by year.

The Illumination of Hidden Paths

Beneath the canopy of stars,
Mysteries beckon near,
Footsteps light on dewy grass,
Where twilight shapes the sphere.

Each corner turned reveals anew,
A world cloaked in surprise,
Silent secrets softly call,
Under moonlit skies.

The hidden paths weave stories old,
Through branches tightly spun,
In the hush of night they stir,
Till the first light of the sun.

Wonders lie in waits unseen,
For eyes that choose to roam,
In the illumination of night,
Every step feels like home.

So follow where the shadows fade,
With courage and with heart,
In the dance of dark and light,
Every journey is art.

Luminous Reveries in the Twilight

As dusk paints skies in shades of gold,
A dreamscape starts to bloom,
Where echoes of laughter can be heard,
In the twilight's gentle room.

Luminous reveries call to souls,
To wander far and wide,
Between the realms of night and day,
Where hidden wishes hide.

Whimsical whispers guide the way,
Through fields of silver grass,
Each moment a precious treasure,
That time cannot surpass.

In the fold of cozy shadows,
Stories begin to play,
An enchanting glow of memories,
In the slow dance of the day.

With every heartbeat and every sigh,
Embrace the calm delight,
For in the luminous twilight,
All is wondrous and bright.